# Magic Mates

## and the
## Puppy Panic

Jane West

Illustrated by
*Stik*

**RISING ★ STARS**

**Rising Stars UK Ltd.**
22 Grafton Street, London W1S 4EX
www.risingstars-uk.com

The right of Jane West to be identified as the author of this work
has been asserted by her in accordance with the Copyright, Design
and Patents Act 1988.

Published 2008

Text, design and layout © Rising Stars UK Ltd.

Cover design: Button plc
Illustrator: Stik, Bill Greenhead for Illustration
Text design and typesetting: Andy Wilson
Publisher: Gill Budgell
Editor: Jane Wood

British Library Cataloguing in Publication Data.
A CIP record for this book is available from the British Library

ISBN: 978 1 84680 327 7

Printed in the UK by CPI Bookmarque, Croydon, CR0 4TD

**Mixed Sources**
Product group from well-managed
forests and other controlled sources
www.fsc.org  Cert no. TT-COC-002227
© 1996 Forest Stewardship Council
FSC

# Contents

# Meet the Magic Mates

The Magic Mates are best friends –
but that doesn't mean they're all alike.

**Name:** 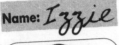 *Izzie*

**The sporty one:** can climb trees, surf and take on the boys at their own game – and win.

**Travels by:** running!

**Loves:** trendy tracksuits, open skies and sandy beaches.

**Hates:** standing still.

**Name:** *Meena*

**The girly one:** uses her mobile for networking and planning her social life.

**Travels by:** Mum's car (her personal chauffeur).

**Loves:** pink and her Magic Mates.

**Hates:** breaking a nail.

**Name:** *Ginger*

**The ginger one:** you don't wanna mess with this feisty gal – the Kung Fu and quick quip queen!

**Travels by:** push-scooter.

**Loves:** Jackie Chan and her Magic Mate pals.

**Hates:** nail extensions.

**Name:** Jo

**The clever one:** uses her brains and quick wit to talk her way out of trouble. Sometimes she's a bit too quick.

**Travels by:** bicycle and is designing a pair of motorised rollerblades.

**Loves:** Jacqueline Wilson, Cathy Cassidy and Albert Einstein.

**Hates:** being called 'geek', 'nerd', 'swot' or 'boffin'.

**Name:** Ellie

**The fashion-conscious one:** can tell her Prada from her Asda and knows how to accessorise.

**Travels by:** limousine, of course! (But only in her dreams.)

**Loves:** shopping.

**Hates:** anything to do with getting dirty; anyone who upsets her Magic Mates.

**Name:** Yash

**The funky punky one:** the 'alternative' one of the gang who hugs trees, people and furry animals.

**Travels by:** skateboard.

**Loves:** having a good time.

**Hates:** bullies.

# The Cutest Puppy in the Whole World

Yash's cousin has a new puppy
called Poppy. Yash invites
the Magic Mates to come and see
the cutest puppy in the whole world.

**Meena**    She's absolutely gorgeous! Look at her tiny little paws!

**Ellie**    I love her fur! It's all white and black. Spots are really fashionable, too.

**Izzie**    Can I cuddle her? Ahhh!

**Yash**    Her name is Poppy. My cousin asked me to look after her for a while.

**Jo**      Look! She's happy to see us.
Her tail is wagging like mad.

**Ginger**      I think Poppy wants to play.
Let's throw a ball for her
in the garden.

Ginger and Poppy run into the garden.
Ginger starts throwing a ball for Poppy.

**Ginger**      Come on, Poppy!
Chase the ball!

9

**Meena**    Don't tire her out too much.
She's only a baby.

**Ginger**    Puppies need exercise –
especially a terrier.

**Ellie**    I bet she is a little terror!

**Yash**    She's a Jack Russell terrier – but
my cousin says she's a real
terror, too!

**Jo**     That's probably because she likes chewing things. When a puppy's teeth start to grow, they feel better if they chew things.

**Izzie**  Yes, that's right. Babies do that, too.

Ginger and Yash play with Poppy until she gets tired. Poppy lies down in the sunshine. Jo and Izzie help Yash to get some drinks and biscuits. Ellie and Meena look at a magazine and Jo reads a book.

| | |
|---|---|
| **Yash** | Where's Poppy?<br>Where did she go? |
| **Jo** | She was here a minute ago.<br>She must have gone inside. |
| **Ellie** | I'll look upstairs. |
| **Meena** | I'll help you. |
| **Jo** | I'll check the kitchen.<br>Poppy probably just got hungry. |

**Izzie**   I'll check the rest of the house.

**Yash** (biting her lip)
I was supposed to be looking
after her.

**Ginger**   Don't worry. We'll find her.
We'll all help you.
Er … you don't think she
could have got out of that hole
in the fence, do you?

Ginger and Yash stare at the fence.
It has a puppy-sized hole in it.

# On the Puppy Trail

Ginger and Yash are looking for puppy Poppy. But which way did she go?

**Yash**    Poppy might have gone to the park. She likes playing with the squirrels.

**Ginger**    We'll be faster with wheels. You get your skateboard and I'll get my scooter.

The girls zoom off to the park.

**Yash**      We have to find Poppy!

**Ginger**   Don't worry. We'll find her.
She's only been gone a minute.
She can't get into trouble that
quickly.

**Yash**      There's the Park Keeper.
Let's ask if he's seen her.

**Ginger**    Excuse me!

Have you seen a puppy?

**Park Keeper**

Yes, lots.

**Yash**    Our puppy is called Poppy.

She's white with black spots.

She's a terrier.

**Park Keeper**

I've seen a Manchester Terrier,

a Scottish Terrier,

a Skye Terrier,

a Tenterfield Terrier,

a Tibetan Terrier,

a Titan Terrier,

a Wheaten Terrier

and a Transylvanian Hound.

I've never heard of a

Poppy Terrier.

**Yash**    Er … thanks.

**Ginger**    Let's go up and down
and look for her.

**Yash**    I've got some Gravybone
dog biscuits. Poppy always
comes when she smells these.

Ginger and Yash go through the park.
They call Poppy's name and wave
the Gravybone biscuits.

**Ginger**    Look! It's Meena's Nan!
Let's ask her if she's seen Poppy.

**Yash**    Excuse me, we're friends
of Meena's and we're looking
for our puppy. She's white
with black spots and floppy ears.
Have you seen her?

**Meena's Nan**

Hello, girls. Yes, I have seen
a puppy like that. She was
with some children. I think
they went down by the lake.

**Yash**    Thanks, loads!

# Hot Dog

Yash and Ginger are really worried.
Poppy is only a few months old.
They don't know if she can swim.
And who are the strange children
that Poppy was with?

The girls zoom down to the lake.
It's hot, and they've been rushing
around.

**Ginger**   Phew! I'm really hot.

**Yash**   Me too. If Poppy is hot,
she might have gone to the lake
for a drink of water.
I hope it's not very deep.
I don't know if Poppy can swim.

**Ginger**   Don't worry, Yash.
We'll find her. Let's ask
that man selling burgers
if he's seen her.

**Yash**    Excuse me, have you seen
a black and white puppy?

**Man**    No, but I've seen a hot dog.
Ha ha! Sorry, girls.
I can see you're upset,
but I'm afraid I haven't
seen your puppy.

**Yash**     Oh no! I can see something
             floating in the lake!

**Ginger**   Be careful!
             Don't go too near the edge!

Yash goes to see what is in the lake.

**Yash**     It's Poppy's ball.
             It means that she's been here.

**Ginger**  She can't be far away.
Come on. Let's look
by those trees. You said Poppy
likes chasing squirrels.

# Hound
# of the Baskervilles

The girls go over to the trees.
But they're stopped in their tracks
by a big dog. It's really big.
Bigger than big. Really, really big.
The biggest dog they've ever seen.

**Yash**        What is that?

**Ginger**    It's either a horse with sharp teeth – or a really big dog!

**Yash**    It's the Hound of the Baskervilles. It's looking at us.

**Ginger**    That's because we look like two snacks!

**Yash**    I think we should back away slowly.

**Ginger**    You back away slowly. I'm going to run!

**Yash** (urgently)

> Don't run! If you run,
> it will only want to chase you!

**Ginger**    I've got an idea! Throw the
Gravybone dog biscuits over
there. We can escape while it
eats them.

The girls get away whilst the Hound of
the Baskervilles tucks into the dog biscuits.

# 5

# Puppy Love

Yash and Ginger are out of breath.
They've looked everywhere in the park
but they still can't find Poppy.

**Ginger**  We've looked everywhere.
I don't think Poppy is here.

**Yash**  But she *was* here.
We found her ball.

**Ginger**   Well, she's not here now.
Where else she might go?

**Yash**   I don't know. Oh, this is awful!
Poor little Poppy! What will
my cousin say? We'd better go
back to the house and get
the others to help us.

**Ginger**   Hang on a minute.
What's going on over there?

**Ginger**  I've never seen so many dogs.
It must be the local dog show.

**Yash**  You're right! My cousin
was talking about it.

**Ginger**  Do you think Poppy has gone
to say hello to the other dogs?
She is very friendly.

**Yash**  Let's go and see if we can
find her.

The girls rush over to the dog show.
The judges are sitting in a big tent.
The dogs are trotting round in a circle.

**Ginger**    I've never seen so many dogs.
There are big dogs, small dogs,
fluffy dogs, scruffy dogs,
brown dogs, white dogs,
black dogs and some dogs
that are all colours.

**Yash**   But I can't see Poppy.

**Judge**   And now we have
the competition for the dog
with the waggiest tail.
Please make your way
to the judging circle.

**Ginger**   Isn't that ...?

**Yash**   Poppy!

A small boy is leading Poppy round
the circle. Poppy's tail is wagging so fast,
it looks like she has at least two tails!

**Yash**      It's Poppy!
            Where did you find her?

**Small boy** She followed us in the park.
            My brother said we shouldn't
            leave her by herself.
            He thought she'd run away
            from the dog show
            so we came here.

**Yash**    Thank you so much!
We were so worried.

**Ginger**    Oh, Poppy! I'm so glad
we found you!

**Yash**    Here, have a Gravybone
to celebrate!

**Ginger**    No thanks! I'd rather
have an ice cream!

**Yash**    Duh!

**Judge**      And the prize for the dog
with the waggiest tail is …
Poppy! Will Poppy
and her owner please come
and receive their prizes.

**Ginger**      That's you, Yash! Go on!

**WAGGIEST TAIL IN SHOW**

*Awarded to....*

*Poppy*

1ST

**Judge**   Well done, Poppy.
Well done to you, too,
young lady. You've got a very
friendly dog there. It's lovely
to see a puppy who is so happy.
Here's a certificate for you
and a pink rosette for Poppy.
Congratulations.

35

**Yash**  Gosh! Thank you very much!

**Ginger**  Poppy looks so sweet
with her pink rosette
but I think she's tired out
from all her adventures.

**Yash**  She really made us panic.

**Ginger**  Well, she's safe now.

**Yash**  Thank you for helping me
find her.

**Ginger**    What are friends for?
I do like a happy ending.

**Yash**    It's what you'd call a story
with a twist in the tale – or tail!

# About the Author

Jane West didn't make up
the dog with the waggiest tail prize.
Dog shows really do have prizes for
the waggiest tail! Her dog Pip hasn't won
the waggiest tail yet, but she did win the
prettiest puppy prize once.

Jane West:

- lives by the beach in Cornwall
- likes taking her dog Pip paddling
  in the sea
- loves bodyboarding
- has worked in an art gallery,
  a bookshop and a school.

Now she's a writer, and has had great fun
writing about the Magic Mates. She hopes you
liked reading about them.

# Looking After Your Puppy

## Do ...

 Do get puppy checked by a vet. They need their injections before their first walk.

 Do have your puppy microchipped. If they get lost, it will help you find them again.

 Do walk your puppy twice a day for about 20 minutes. When they get older and stronger, you can take them for longer walks.

 Do feed your dog proper puppy food.

 Do train your puppy. There are lots of schools to help you, and it's fun! Try: www.puppyschool.co.uk.

 Do pick up your puppy's poo when you take it for a walk. It's not much fun, but it's worse if someone treads in it! Yeuch!

## Don't ...

- Don't forget to walk your puppy. Think how you would feel if you had to stay in all day with no one to play with. It's just the same for your puppy!

- Don't give your puppy any chocolate or sweets. It's bad for them and could make them very sick.

To find out more about looking after a puppy, go to www.dogstrust.org.uk.

# Famous Dogs

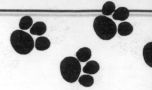

### Greyfriars Bobby

Bobby was a Skye Terrier. He was a very loyal
little dog. When his owner, John Gray, died,
Bobby would not leave the graveyard where
he was buried. He lived in the graveyard for the
next 14 years, fed by friendly local shopkeepers.

### Nipper

Nipper is the dog on the recording label for
HMV. HMV stands for 'His Master's Voice'
because it has a picture of Nipper listening to
a voice on an old-fashioned record player.

### Fluffy

Do you remember who had to get past Fluffy,
the three-headed dog? Harry Potter in
*Harry Potter and the Philosopher's Stone.*

### Toto

Toto was Dorothy's dog in *The Wizard of Oz*.

### Lassie

The first film about Lassie was made in about 1942. Lassie was a clever Collie dog who helped people. Sometimes Lassie has been played by boy dogs!

### Lady and Tramp

The cartoonist Walt Disney had a poodle called Lady. He later went on to make the cartoon film called *Lady and the Tramp*. It was about a well-bred dog, Lady, who meets a rough street dog called Tramp.

### Old Shep

Elvis Presley was just eight years old when he first sang in public. The song was 'Old Shep', about a boy and his sheepdog.

# Dog Record-Breakers

 The Greyhound is the fastest dog. It can run at 45 miles per hour.

 The Irish Wolfhound is the largest dog.

 The Great Dane is the tallest dog.

 The Chihuahua is the smallest dog. (chee-wow-wa)

 The Saint Bernard is the heaviest dog.

What do you get if you cross a Terrier with a Bulldog?

I don't know, but I think it would be terribull!

# Did You Know?

- Dalmatian puppies are white when they are born. Their spots appear later.

- A dog can hear sounds 250 metres away. A person can't hear much beyond 25 metres.

- Dogs have twice as many muscles for moving their ears as people. Can you move your ears?

- In its first week, a puppy spends 90% of the time sleeping and 10% eating – sounds good to me!

- A puppy's adult teeth start to come through between four and eight months, when it starts to chew everything. And I mean everything!

# Puppy Quiz

1 How often should you walk your puppy?

2 What should you feed your puppy?

3 How much of a puppy's time is spent sleeping in its first week?

4 When do a puppy's adult teeth start coming through?

5 Why shouldn't you feed your puppy chocolate?

## Answers

5 It's bad for them and could make them very sick.
4 Four to eight months.
3 90%.
2 Puppy food.
1 Twice a day

# Puppy Lingo

**Sit**  Boring

**Stay**  Very boring

**Walkies**  Yeaaaay!

**Playtime**  Yeaaaay!

**Dinner**  Yeaaaay!

**No**  You don't mean that, 'cos I'm so cute.

• • • • • • • • • • • • • • • • • • • • • • • • • • • • • •

## How did you score?

**0–1**  Oh dear! I think the puppy had better look after *you*!

**2–3**  Not bad, but you've got a bit more to learn about looking after a puppy.

**4–5**  You're ready to be a puppy pal!

# Magic Mates

 and the Beach Babes

 and the Battle of the Bullies

 Go Wild!

 and the Holiday of Horrors

 in Hollywood

 and the Jungle Drums

 and the Big Knickers Scandal

 Meet the Masterpiece

 and the Moody Monday

 and the Puppy Panic

 and the Revenge of the Vegetables

 with Stars in their Eyes

# RISING ★ STARS

Magic Mates books are available from most booksellers.

For mail order information
please call Rising Stars on 0871 47 23 010
or visit www.risingstars-uk.com